NB   Mix 'n' Match   —   Christmas.

(Philip Sparke?)

A. Wright

CW00542280

Christmas Razzamajazz clarinet

A. Wright

The fun way to learn!

Christmas Razzamajazz
clarinet

SARAH WATTS

kevin mayhew

We hope you enjoy the music in this book.
Further copies of this and our many other books are available
from your local Kevin Mayhew stockist.

In case of difficulty, or to request a catalogue,
please contact the publisher direct by writing to:

The Sales Department
KEVIN MAYHEW LTD
Buxhall
Stowmarket
Suffolk IP14 3BW

Phone 01449 737978
Fax 01449 737834
E-mail info@kevinmayhewltd.com

First published in Great Britain in 2003 by Kevin Mayhew Ltd.

© Copyright 2003 Kevin Mayhew Ltd.

ISBN 1 84417 096 9
ISMN M 57024 210 8
Catalogue No: 3611752

0 1 2 3 4 5 6 7 8 9

The music in this book is protected by copyright and may not be reproduced
in any way for sale or private use without the consent of the copyright owner.

Cover design: Angela Selfe
Music setter: Tracy Cook
Proof reader: Marian Hellen

Printed and bound in Great Britain

Contents

ON SILENT NIGHTS

© Copyright 2003 Kevin Mayhew Ltd.

It is illegal to photocopy music.

THREE SWINGIN' SHIPS!

© Copyright 2003 Kevin Mayhew Ltd.
It is illegal to photocopy music.

GOD REST YE!

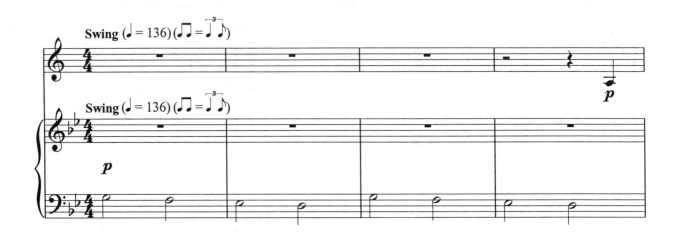

© Copyright 2003 Kevin Mayhew Ltd.

It is illegal to photocopy music.

AWAY

© Copyright 2003 Kevin Mayhew Ltd.
It is illegal to photocopy music.

A. Wright
c/o Rebecca
Rawson.

Christmas Razzamajazz
clarinet

SARAH WATTS

ON SILENT NIGHTS

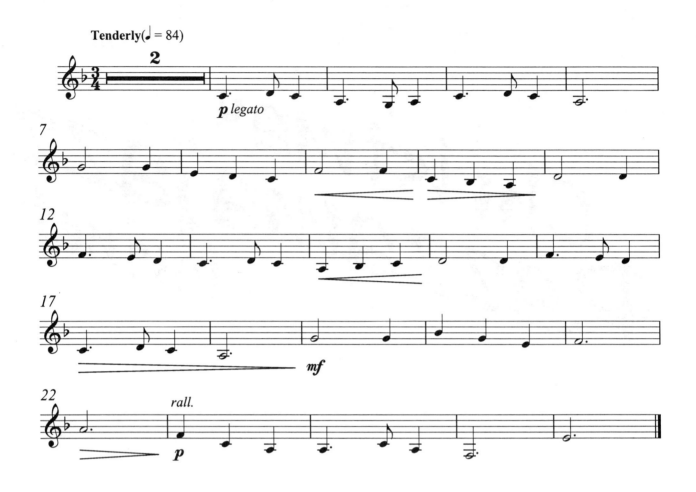

THREE SWINGIN' SHIPS!

© Copyright 2003 Kevin Mayhew Ltd.
It is illegal to photocopy music.

GOD REST YE!

© Copyright 2003 Kevin Mayhew Ltd.

It is illegal to photocopy music.

AWAY

© Copyright 2003 Kevin Mayhew Ltd.
It is illegal to photocopy music.

DISTANT SLEIGHS

© Copyright 2003 Kevin Mayhew Ltd.

It is illegal to photocopy music.

CLEARLY MIDNIGHT

© Copyright 2003 Kevin Mayhew Ltd.
It is illegal to photocopy music.

HOLLY AND IVY

Continue to play this pattern while your partner
improvises using any of the notes below (they will all fit!)
Improvise for 12 bars each. Swap parts on repeat.

© Copyright 2003 Kevin Mayhew Ltd.
It is illegal to photocopy music.

GOOD KING SWINGSATLAST!

© Copyright 2003 Kevin Mayhew Ltd.

It is illegal to photocopy music.

KINGS SWING!

© Copyright 2003 Kevin Mayhew Ltd.
It is illegal to photocopy music.

JOY!

© Copyright 2003 Kevin Mayhew Ltd.

It is illegal to photocopy music.

kevin
mayhew

Kevin Mayhew Limited • Buxhall • Stowmarket • Suffolk • IP14 3BW • UK

www.kevinmayhew.com

DISTANT SLEIGHS

© Copyright 2003 Kevin Mayhew Ltd.
It is illegal to photocopy music.

CLEARLY MIDNIGHT

© Copyright 2003 Kevin Mayhew Ltd.
It is illegal to photocopy music.

HOLLY AND IVY

© Copyright 2003 Kevin Mayhew Ltd.

It is illegal to photocopy music.

13

2nd time to Coda ⊕

2nd time to Coda ⊕

Continue to play this pattern while your partner
improvises using any of the notes below (they will all fit!)
Improvise for twelve bars each. Swap parts on repeat.

17

21

20

2nd time D.S. al Coda

2nd time D.S. al Coda

29 CODA

CODA

GOOD KING SWINGSATLAST!

© Copyright 2003 Kevin Mayhew Ltd.
It is illegal to photocopy music.

23

KINGS SWING!

© Copyright 2003 Kevin Mayhew Ltd.
It is illegal to photocopy music.

25

D.S. al Coda ⊕ CODA

JOY!

© Copyright 2003 Kevin Mayhew Ltd.
It is illegal to photocopy music.